FOUR CORNERS OF GRACE

When You Hear, "It's Cancer"

David Staal and Becky Staal

Book
Corner
Publishing

"A cancer diagnosis – as a nurse, I experienced this many times with my patients and their families. I have walked alongside countless friends and close family members – and faced it myself twice. I have searched for words and reflections that I can gift; words that will afford some measure of support, comfort, and courage to others. David and Becky Staal's **Four Corners of Grace** is what I have searched for. Sharing David's own story reinforces that he has true insight. Inviting reflections from others who have supported the journey with him, or had their own journey, adds true reality. Early in the book, a Bible verse sets the essence of David's message that will lift up many, *'....yet I still dare to hope....the faithful love of the Lord never ends.'*"

— Cynthia McCurren, PhD, RN
Dean and Professor, School of Nursing, University of Michigan-Flint

"As an author, counselor, and husband of a cancer survivor, I found David and Becky Staal's **Four Corners of Grace** extremely helpful and insightful. The personal experiences and stories shared allow readers to explore their feelings and struggles accompanied by a wonderful guide and helpful perspective. This book has great depth with biblical truths, while still being easily accessible. I highly recommend this resource for anyone touched by cancer."

— Peter Newhouse, PhD, LMSW
CEO, Winning At Home

"In **Four Corners of Grace**, David and Becky Staal gracefully give permission to think, feel, ask, and speak all the things we have unfortunately convinced ourselves may not be okay to think, feel, ask, or speak with a blunt vulnerability that had me tearing up, chuckling, aching, and praising. They share applicable practices to approach the various physical, emotional, and spiritual challenges of a cancer diagnosis and treatment journey with candor and a good dose of quiet humor. A must-read for both cancer warriors and caregivers."

— Dr. Maria McCormick, DNP, CPNP
Dean of the College of Nursing, Baker College

"Four Corners of Grace supports the cancer patients, caregivers, and families we work with through our ministry. So many individuals will benefit from reading this book because the stories are personal and meaningful, sharing strengths and weaknesses in ways sure to help people on a journey that David and Becky traveled. Their book will serve as an important resource for our program."

— Martha Webb, Our Journey of Hope Cancer Care
Minister
Port City Church

"Four Corners of Grace is a gem! David and Becky Staal's take on cancer is not theoretical – they walked the very road they write about. From beginning to end, the book sets forth the challenges facing cancer patients in realistic fashion, pulling no punches about the difficulty of this journey. But they do not leave the reader without hope…far from it! They offer time-tested guidance gleaned from friends struggling with cancer and their own experience. Anyone facing adversity of any kind can benefit from the many nuggets of wisdom packed into this book."

— Reverend David Hughes, PhD
Ambassador, Transforming Center

Four Corners of Grace: When you hear, "It's cancer"

Book interior design by Elise Sagmoe
Cover design by ENS Photography, ensphotography.net

ISBN (softcover) 978-1-7343509-4-4
ISBN (e-format) 978-1-7343509-5-1

Book
Corner
Publishing

FourCornersofGrace.com

TABLE OF CONTENTS

And Yet

-Journey-

SOME words crash land.

I drove home instead of to work following a medical appointment that felt like a swerve offroad and into a ditch. The appointment, not the drive. A doctor had explained the hostile results from a routine biopsy. After his long description, he detected my confusion. He moved his chair in close for emphasis and said, "I don't know what you have going on in life right now – but you need to press pause on everything and fight for your life."

A heavy, crushing statement by any measure.

Once back home and just a couple steps inside the door, my wife Becky asked, "What are you doing home?"

"Well," I said, struggling to find the right words. Or any words.

The silence caused her to sense a problem. She asked, "How was the doctor?"

"It's cancer."

The gravity that those two words carry feels unbearable – to say, to hear, even to type. In that moment, life changed. Because you're holding this book, I know life has changed for you, too.

A new journey began for our family, one that we didn't choose. Who would? Confusing, complicated, and completely void of advance warning – cancer follows no rules and involves unfamiliar, multi-syllable words hard to pronounce and even harder to understand. Or to accept.

A cancer diagnosis can force a person down a dark, unlit path toward an unknown destination. For that reason, consider this book a flashlight. Hope exists; we simply need to shine a light to find it. Hope for what? Keep reading.

Back when the diagnosis arrived, our son Scott and daughter Erin (now adults) were just six and three years old. But even for them, cancer caused life to twist and turn. Similar to how the disease overwhelms healthy cells, cancer arrives and destroys normality for everyone, including entire families.

And yet, it's possible to let go of the old normal and look for a new version. Could it be that the optimistic approach "seek and you will find" can work in your situation like it did in mine?

Yes, it can.

Our family chose to cherish words, savor moments, celebrate big wins or small gains – and to laugh. Defiantly at times, but always deliberately. You can make life-giving choices too. For me, the journey started with a clear conviction: Cancer would have to take my life because I was determined not to willingly give it up. To engage this battle, hope would function as the fuel and grace would serve as our weapon of choice. After all, the doctor said to fight for my life.

A battle worth waging, right?

Someone likely gave you this book because they care about you and your well-being. These pages provide opportunities to rest your heart, recalibrate your attitude, and renew your outlook. You'll need all of those to fight well. To that end, you will encounter more clarity than cleverness; more authenticity than authority. What you won't find is advice on how to treat your cancer. Every case is unique and personal. Instead, expect guidance on how to live well. Or at least better. Some ideas won't necessarily apply to you or your situation –

that's fine because the book is short and fast-paced, meaning we won't stay on any topic for very long.

This is the book I wish someone had handed to me when my journey started. Not because it contains answers. It doesn't. Not because it contains expert advice. It doesn't. Its greatest value comes from the encouragement woven into the lone absolute found in this book: *You must figure out how to always keep going.* Standing still is not an option if you want to still be standing at your battle's conclusion. Expect to receive frequent reminders of this truth. Take them to heart.

We're in this together. I've heard the diagnosis you heard, sat in the waiting rooms you visit, faced similar choices, prayed the same prayers, cried the same tears, and pretended to be brave and strong and confident – until fatigue shut down the charade. Or the sickness did. Odd how much it took to finally make peace with the tender, scared, honest me. You have permission to let the honest, real you read this book and linger on the pages awhile. Nobody can fully prepare to hear "It's cancer."

You and I, as fellow travelers, will share a transparent conversation. Life with cancer often proves physically, mentally, and emotionally draining. Or, to use blunter language, it sucks. Agreed?

Yet, grace has this way of helping us navigate all that – and more. You have choices to make, choices prompted less by what the disease does and more about how you decide your life will proceed.

Equipped with that belief, we will take a deep and honest dive into topics and say things you might not hear from anyone else – but that you likely think, feel, or want to scream. That's fine. Grace doesn't shush reality, make cheap excuses, or force-feed ideas about what to do to make this nightmare go away. Nope. Grace isn't a different pathway to take, it's a new way to walk whatever path you're already on. To help you keep going when so many reasons exist for you to stop.

You must keep going. Say it to yourself – *I must keep going*. Now say it again.

Two good friends, Lisa and Lori, have agreed to join us. Lisa, a career public school educator, lives in suburban Chicago. Lori – a lifelong volleyball player, fan, and coach – calls Orlando home. They will share perspectives that branch out in different directions yet remain rooted in the common ground we share. You'll appreciate their candor. My battle took place years ago. Lisa and Lori will receive chemo treatments this week. Both view their contributions to this book as ways to more fully live and fight and help others do the same. Yes, sharing their journeys will help them to keep going. What an honor to walk with them.

A few promises before our hike through this book begins: No preaching. No prescribing. No suggested cures. Just clear ideas about how grace can light the way. No sugar-coated hype to artificially motivate you or make cancer sound like it's a great opportunity. Plenty of other books do all that. This one will steady you enough to help you sleep a little better, smile a little more, and breathe without sighing so much. At the end of this book, you will still have a cancer battle to fight, so let's remain realistic.

And yet, you will develop a new and unflappable grace about you. As a result, expect grace to usher in hope – and close behind the arrival of hope comes peace.

Peace would likely feel pretty good right now. When it arrives, expect people around you to wonder how you do it. Grace and hope and peace during a cancer fight show a triplex dimension rarely seen in someone facing a serious challenge. But it's possible, and you can prove it.

To point us in the right direction, let's first consider "grace" to represent the way we react (or don't react) to a situation – in a manner that produces goodwill in your own heart first and in others' hearts second. The chapters that follow will add to this working definition.

Ancient wisdom has much to say about grace. Although the Bible contains text written thousands of years ago, it shares words that articulate well what a frustrated heart might long to cry out in this very moment:

I will never forget this awful time, as I grieve
over my loss.

Yet I still dare to hope when I remember this:
The faithful love of the LORD never ends!
His mercies never cease.
Lamentations 3:20-22 (NLT)

Four Corners of Grace

So let us come boldly to the throne of our gracious
God. There we will receive his mercy, and we will
find grace to help us when we need it most.

Hebrews 4:16 (NLT)

Right here and right now qualifies as "when we need it most," right?

Rooms typically include four distinct corners – as does a high-definition picture of grace. We will visit each corner long enough to become familiar with the grace it offers – grace that is readily available for you. Visits worth making, my friend, for good reason. The time you'll spend reading these pages will prove to be the best investment you will make in yourself for a long, long time.

To serve a group of overlooked heroes, Becky wrote the book's last section for caregivers.

Share a copy with whomever serves in that role for you and write "Thank you" on that chapter's title page. This is your chance to hand a gift to an angel.

Use the page that ends each chapter to write your responses to questions, related ideas that come to mind as you read, or other notes. A book must offer space for the reader to record his or her thoughts if it seeks to feel conversational, right?

Much of the road ahead falls outside of your ability to control. Or even to completely understand. Life will feel chaotic because cancer creates tension between reality and hope. No case is hopeless, yet no cure is guaranteed. Nor is tomorrow. *For anyone*. Remember, grace can't eliminate the journey you're on, but it can improve how you navigate that journey.

Together, we will take a well-lit path, at times illuminated by statements that signal hope and start with "**And yet**." Look for them. Our journey starts when we turn the next page – and we find the first corner.

Let's go.

Words and phrases that describe how I feel – physically and emotionally – right now:

Four Corners of Grace

Grace for Me

-Permission-

CANCER arrives randomly; sometimes easy to discover, other times challenging to detect. Some cases prove mild. Others, terminal. Some have a clear path forward for treatment options. Others take unexpected turns. Nearly everyone feels some degree of shock because the diagnosis frequently comes as a surprise. The thought "I'm not ready for this" serves as an indicator that you possess honest self-awareness.

Honesty is a wonderful place from which to start a journey, even when it involves surprise.

That was true of Lori, our fellow cancer fighter introduced earlier. She says, "Our daughter was about to finish college, and our son had just graduated from high school. The long-awaited empty nest years had finally arrived, but I never pictured a health threat entering our lives this early on."

Good point, Lori. Why would anyone picture such a thing?

In my case, I didn't notice anything physically wrong before hearing I had cancer. It was the stomach-turning news that made me feel awful. Maybe you share a similar experience: An uninvited, unwelcome, and hard to understand new reality enters the story and – from the first moment, before any treatments or health declines – just the idea of cancer creates internal chaos. The following excerpts from my daily journal, thoughts jotted down in the first few days that followed my diagnosis, might sound familiar to you:

David's Journal

February 15
I feel freaked out by the sad, almost grief-stricken look on people's faces when they see me. They look

at me like I'm dying. It's funny how even a lousy joke relieves the tension. But is it funny?

February 17

My mind races with dark thoughts about what's going to happen; I don't feel comfortable telling anyone about it because they will think I'm losing my mind or just feeling sorry for myself. Maybe I am?

February 23

I'd really like to tell people I'm deeply scared and really don't want to talk about it when they ask how I'm doing. The honest answer: I don't know how I'm doing.

March 1

*It's 4 a.m. and everyone else in the world is asleep
except me because I can't stop thinking about what's
ahead. I just want to know. Wait, maybe I don't. Is
this all a bad dream?*

Like sharp turns on a switchback trail, thoughts,
reactions, and emotions show up and force you in
different directions. Take a deep breath and expect
to struggle with more than the physical disease.
Now is a good moment to tell yourself words that
will set you free:

I need to give myself grace.

You might want to say that out loud. Right now.

Next, articulate *your* it's-okay-to-struggle
thoughts about cancer. Write about them (a page for

this is provided at this chapter's end), go for a walk to say them aloud, doodle them on paper, sit with a friend and ask them to just listen. But don't let such thoughts wander around your mind on their own.

Why? Because when dark fears loiter inside you, they shoplift valuable energy and rob your ability to think about anything else. Bring them into the open and prepare to feel relief. Self-honesty purchases moments of internal peace, so repeat the process whenever needed.

And yet, we're just getting started. Giving yourself grace can do much more for you.

Early in my journey, holistic advice from an oncologist sounded wholly unrealistic: "To battle cancer well requires you to eliminate stress from your life."

Got it, no stress. Is that a joke? Realistically, it seems like wishful thinking; how can it happen? Good question.

Answer: Through the deep grace experienced by giving yourself permission. Specifically, permit yourself to develop willpower, resilience, and diversion. These three serve as building blocks for additional permissions that will make grace for yourself become real.

Willpower is the all-encompassing, all-in attitude that produces energy and drive. No one can give willpower to someone else; it all comes from within you.

Give yourself permission to develop confidence that you *can* win the battle ahead, fueled by a stubborn commitment to life and an insistence that one day cancer *will* be behind you. Give yourself permission to look to the future, to talk about better times ahead, and to celebrate victories big and small. Winning a battle against cancer rarely happens through a single, oh-my-gosh-its-gone miracle. The far more likely reality to unfold involves small wins that build upon one another. One good test result, then another, and so on. Yes, that will take time and drain energy. Regardless of physical strength levels, though, internal willpower can serve as the pure determination needed to keep going.

Resilience means refusal to hand one's existence over to cancer. If this disease wants your life, it will have to battle you for it.

Give yourself permission to fight. Quite likely,

you'll receive both good news and bad news at various times along the way. Resilience proves invaluable when plans and expectations wash away, just as it enables celebration when bright moments appear. Plenty of waiting will take place for test results, treatment efficacy, healing, appointments, the list runs long. Plan on it. When you pre-determine how you will travel the journey and then react according to your terms, you retain control. Self-permission to develop stubbornness becomes a useful tool, especially stubborn optimism, stubborn resolve, and stubborn focus.

On a much-needed and lighter note, give yourself permission to laugh, and you'll discover surprising strength for the journey. Share reasons to chuckle and then watch resilience turn contagious, infecting anyone close. People enjoy a cancer person's humor, whether funny or lame, because it's a welcome interruption that decreases the tension.

Diversion refers to times when you've had enough of all the cancer stuff, so you occupy your time and attention with something else.

Give yourself permission to deliberately ignore the disease for as long as necessary to catch your breath and regain energy. In moments of denial, you'll remember who you were before the diagnosis. Cancer does not deserve the right to redefine you, but it will try. View diversion as exercising your ability to turn attention elsewhere. For example, give yourself permission to take a break from talking about it and, when needed, even thinking about it. Go away for a weekend. Or for a long walk. Read a book for enjoyment, rather than to learn more about the disease or treatment options. Take an extended break from social media to avoid the constant ads, suggestions, and other reminders that will constantly push at you. If you must engage with a screen, use one to plan a getaway trip or to text friends and ask how they're doing. Focusing on others, even for just a few brief moments, provides refreshing respite. So does the beauty of a sunset or a favorite movie. With a tub of buttered popcorn.

Back to reality: Willpower, resilience, and diversion don't develop on their own. They happen by deliberate choice, not by chance, and over time. Anything worth having is worth working for. Start now.

Four Corners of Grace

And yet, soon you'll find that more self-permissions now prove easier to adopt, delivering grace for you in greater abundance. Let's examine a few that will enable you to breathe easier, doubt yourself less, and provide assurance that you are not crazy.

I give myself the grace to avoid comparing cancers.

Even when others make the comparison. "My radiation oncologist said in twenty-seven years, he had never seen pancreatic cancer go to the bone," says Lisa, our Chicago-based friend introduced earlier.

Maybe medically intriguing, and certainly packing no ill-intent, comments like her doctor shared can deliver discouragement. Your cancer is unique to you. Sure, it's okay to hear about other peoples' experiences. Yes, it can be good to learn from them because something helpful for your battle might turn up. Or it might not. More likely the latter. Fingerprints also seem similar, yet no two are the same. Listen graciously, but filter everything.

Comparisons with other health issues can also prove tempting – but resist those, too. As a personal example, the world seemed to quickly rally around the need to invest in the immediate discovery of treatments and vaccines for COVID to eliminate the need to wear a mask. Yet, I still need to lather with SPF70 and wear long sleeves and a hat whenever the sun shines. Can we please feel similar urgency toward cancer? Breathe and relax, David. Advances in one area of medicine don't necessarily cause diversion from work in other areas. And hey, the new materials used in sun shirts do make them quite comfy. Yes, I continue to develop in these grace areas.

I give myself the grace to focus on myself.

"The truth is that this diagnosis shifted us," says Lori. "My husband and I were drawn to the people, places, and activities we enjoyed most and started eliminating as much of the 'unnecessary' as we could. We even moved out of state."

To battle the disease, of course, you'll need to focus on yourself – and feel absolutely no guilt about doing that. Go ahead and figure out how to enjoy life. To that end, allow cancer to embolden you to do whatever you must. This might sound overly dramatic, but when you believe your days may be numbered, commit to making each one of them count.

I give myself the grace to receive attention and assistance.

Some people love attention. Many don't, especially when battling something like an unpredictable disease. "It's not only hard to ask for help," Lori says, "it's difficult to know what help is needed."

Even people who like to be noticed prefer that it happens for a good reason. When people help one another, though, a rich version of goodness occurs. That said, fight through any negative perceptions that serve as roadblocks, and accept the help.

"My biggest fear is that I am a burden to others," says Lisa. "It's hard to ask for help because it feels like you're accepting that you can't do things for yourself anymore. So, tell yourself that it's temporary, and you will hopefully soon get back to your old self."

Just don't fight cancer alone. At times when you don't have strength, make sure there are strong people nearby on whom you can lean. Find a point person who will help with details when you don't have the strength, attention, or ability to care. We will take a deeper look at other people in the next chapter and at caregivers in the final chapter.

I give myself the grace to not blame myself.

Lisa says, "I kept asking, 'What did I do wrong?' I blamed myself. My doctors said to not look backward, but to look forward and beat this disease."

While frustrating, definitive cause-and-effect does not exist. Research the reasons people have cancer, and the list will run long. Everyone knows about lifestyle choices that cause high risk. Still, not everyone who makes such choices develops cancer. Equally confusing, some people who regularly make healthy choices end up in the oncology center. The same inconsistencies apply to inherited genetics, environmental exposure, and many other factors. What can be gained by blaming anything, especially yourself? The question "Why me?" has no reliable answer. Rather than attempting to pinpoint a reason, use your energy to plan how to travel the path ahead. Nothing in the past can be undone, so focus on what you will do to move forward.

Four Corners of Grace

A focus on the future launches from the life-building decision to give yourself grace, as shown whenever you give yourself permission. Oh sure, dark thoughts will still pay visits, but they will find no room to stay when grace for yourself occupies your mind and heart.

This all sounds good until it's late at night, when minds love to race to extreme places. In those anxious times, grace for yourself can enable you to drift back to sleep. One more of my journal entries will show how grace can deliver quick wins. Cancer involves a journey filled with such moments.

February 10, 2:45 a.m.

When I examine what scares me most, it isn't what might happen to me. No, what I'm scared of more than anything is the thought of leaving my family. If

I'm not around, who will teach Scott how to shoot a jump shot or throw a spiral? Who will coach him into manhood? Who will hold onto Erin as she learns to ride a bike? Who will walk her down the aisle one day?

I will.

I'm walking with her. Whatever I need to do, I'll do. Today. Tomorrow. As long as it takes.

What about you? Make the decision to give yourself permission, and let's keep going.

My it's-okay-to-struggle thoughts about cancer include:

Grace for Others

-Truth-

TELLING people about your cancer is neither easy nor enjoyable. The initial conversation often proves emotional. And yet, it's only the starting point for people interactions. Some will go well. Others make you want to walk away. Or run.

Another option exists.

Four Corners of Grace

The previous chapter began to prepare you for a journey. Now that you've developed grace for yourself, let's explore sharing grace with others. You can only give away what you already possess, so once the necessary equipping has taken place, start doling it out.

"Why focus a chapter on other people when I'm the sick one?" you might ask. The primary reason: Journeys go much better with a companion.

Of course, another person cannot walk even a single step in your shoes. You know it. They know it. So, let's take an honest look at expectations and options for our reactions, which will ensure that we avoid reheating leftover platitudes such as "Life's better with friends."

Counting on life to suddenly turn better for any reason feels unrealistic, considering our topic. Instead, let's shoot for "Life's more navigable with friends" to start. Maybe we'll ascend to "more tolerable" as we match five graces with five hard truths that we will find billboarded along our journey.

Truth #1: *It's not good to be alone, but expect it.*

"One huge enemy when navigating a cancer diagnosis is aloneness," says Lori. "And that includes relationally, physically, medically, and spiritually. Those with cancer need to take steps to avoid loneliness, and the people in their lives can really help."

Too often, though, loneliness prevails. Why? Cancer is a dark and scary place where nobody wants to live or stay any longer than necessary. While others might attempt a visit, they can only watch and wave from the waiting room – they can't step into your reality. Some will try; most will not.

Although you have no choice, you don't want to be here either. At the start of the journey many new activities, words, thoughts, emotions, and decisions descended upon you. Or maybe crashed into you? Either way, it's understandable to want to get away. To hide. At least avoid.

Full disclosure: After journeying with cancer for two decades, I still experience moments when I just don't want to talk about it.

And now Grace for Others #1: *Battling loneliness is as easy as A-B-C.*

A – Admit that loneliness is real; maybe even to be anticipated.

B – Believe that others care about me and that they can make a positive difference in how this journey feels to travel.

C – Choose to stop hiding; to stop feeling afraid of what others think or to feel like an imposition or burden.

I fumbled through the darkness of loneliness for a long time. Finally, I embraced reality: sometimes a person's reaction can isolate me and make me feel alone, even when the person stands just a few feet from me. This reality ushers us toward the next truth.

Truth #2: *Prepare for strange (or worse) interactions.*

Good words prove hard to find in tense moments, but that won't stop folks who feel the need to say something. "When I told people about my diagnosis, the spectrum of responses varied," says Lisa. "Most people were shocked, like my own reaction. Many people didn't know what to say, which I think is common, unless you have gone through it."

Lori admits to feeling particularly sensitive to condescending or 'trying too hard' expressions, especially when someone shares such statements in a group setting – or on a day that has not gone well. For example, she heard a comment while with friends that felt loaded with meaning beyond the words spoken. "I remember one person saying, 'Now Lori, if anything gets difficult today, please let us know.'"

"My inner translation: Just reminding you that all of us are healthy and you, Lori, are sick."

Oh, the comments can turn much stranger. Even close friends and family will respond in ways that stretch from goofy to horrifying. Without realizing what they're saying, some might even come across as killing you early.

Seriously? Yes. A friend sent Lisa this Facebook message: "Lisa, I am beyond words. I know the survival rate for pancreatic cancer is increasing, but your prognosis is not good. I have such wonderful memories of you from our first day on the playground to the last time I saw you at the reunion.

Should you or your family plan anything in your honor, please let me know. I want to celebrate your life with you. What are your future plans? If I were you, I would plan a big vacation and a big party. Let me know if I can help in any way."

Lisa describes feeling shocked and angry. "At first, I couldn't believe he seemed to be planning my funeral without knowing me that well," she says. "I was thinking, 'How dare you make me feel scared and anxious, and how dare you tell me what to do with my time left?'

"Finally, I realized that he didn't know what to say and was only trying to help, albeit in entirely the wrong way. He was kind of clueless, but it wasn't his fault."

In addition to weird comments, many cancer patients must also absorb strange glances. Or stares. While some folks journey through treatment in remarkably discreet appearance, the rest of us take visible hits. Weight loss, color change, missing hair, surgery scars; the list goes on. Many people remain unaware that an extended gaze or curious glance will send nonverbal messages that can make the recipient envy snakes that can shed their skin when needed.

As a person who likely sent such signals before my own cancer journey, whenever crossing paths with someone clearly fighting this disease today, I now think *There's a beautiful soul fighting a hard battle*. Try it; you'll find that sharing an ever-soslight smile – even if unnoticed – provides a healthy self-reminder that your heart is well.

And now Grace for Others #2: *Assume good intentions.*

Lisa shows us tremendous grace in action when she described what happened with her clueless friend, but then realized that he tried. And failed. But at least he tried.

Her internal perspective drives her external kindness. "When people say or do things that aren't what I think sound supportive, I just think to myself, 'They just don't know any better. They haven't gone through this themselves or with someone close to them.'"

Lori agrees. "I believe there is a true desire to communicate care and concern, but most of us are clumsy with this sort of thing."

Grace means extending to people the assumption that no ill-intentions exist. Too often we might assume the opposite is true. Strange words, responses, or looks emerge from a desire to engage – all while emotions overwhelm thoughtfulness and appropriateness. Even fellow cancer patients can fumble for just the right words. When that happens, just respond with a quiet hug. Works every time.

Truth #3: *Options and opinions are everywhere.* Somehow, and for some baffling reason, many people form ideas about how to defeat cancer in others. Get ready; those ideas will come your way.

Unsolicited, too. They arrive in at least five forms (suggested responses are included):

1) Suggested cures that worked for another person. (*Every case is different, thank you.*)

2) Assurance that it's no big deal because someone else had cancer and beat it. (*Glad everything worked out well for them, thank you.*)

3) A steady flow of either "you should…" or "you shouldn't…" directives. (*I'm considering my options, thank you.*)

4) Internet-only educated folks who studied this online but have little or no experience with cancer. (*There is a lot of information out there, thank you.*) In our first appointment, my oncologist said, "Please don't rely on the web."

5) People who hear about my physician's comments in #4 and say, "You see, there's a medical industry/big pharma conspiracy." (*I have no words, thank you.*)

And now Grace for Others #3: *Keep a clear boundary around your eyes, ears, and heart.*

Listen and thank. Quietly forget or ignore when needed. If you know someone will attempt to cure you, and you just don't have the desire to endure someone's opinion and defend yourself (harsh to say, but appropriate when considering that your energy should be spent fighting the disease), the way of grace might be to avoid the encounter.

For digital interactions, maintain a similar grace filter. Read the text or email and send a quick thank you. Keep the message or delete it. The encouraging messages make for good reading whenever you need a lift.

On the topic of online activity, remember that what you consume – whether listening or reading – remains your choice. Researching treatment options makes you a better-informed patient. Cancer has a strange, confusing vernacular, so there's wisdom in learning this new language. But limits must exist.

"The main thing I do is try not to read too much on social media," Lisa says. "Some sites have good information, but they also have some very negative posts about all the people who have died, and that brings me down – or back to reality, since many days I do live in denial."

In-person, in messages, or online, unfortunate encounters can happen at any time. Don't be surprised. During one of my previous employer's annual health insurance meetings, the human resources director described the reason why the medical plan premium would increase and, therefore, cost everyone much more than the year before. "We've had a couple of complicated and very expensive medical cases," he said. I saw a few glances in my direction, while my glare focused on the HR guy.

Sometimes, you just need to speak up.

I approached him after the meeting and asked him to reconsider how he justifies the cost increase. Placing blame on me and another person, which clearly happened, felt terrible. He quickly and repeatedly apologized – and changed his presentation. I felt better after speaking up.

Four Corners of Grace

Lori offers golden direction to find the way of grace: "We're all just doing our best with the life experiences, resources, and energy we have. Most times when people cause hurt and frustration, it's entirely unintentional."

Truth #4: *And yet, some do get it right.*

Prepare to also see goodness emerge. Notice it. Appreciate it. Grab hold of it and squeeze tight. Others' efforts will provide positive energy to help you keep going.

"Many close friends have been amazing in supporting me through all three of my cancer battles," says Lisa. "I couldn't have gotten through these last six years without them."

She lists a few examples that touched her heart and remain in her memory:

- Daily receiving cards that let me know people are thinking of me. (I save them all). One friend sends me cards at least once a week.

- Others text me during the day just to let me know they're thinking about me.

- Thoughtful and useful presents, which touch my heart and help me stay comfy. Soft socks, robes, or inspiring books.

- Fellow teachers donated their sick days this year to cover a full year of employment after my sick days ran out; what compassion!

"People show me how much they care, and along the way, their efforts prove how much I am loved," says Lisa.

Lori has noticed how some people make encounters positive by the manner with which they share their suggested alternatives. For example, she has a friend who fought cancer and thoughtfully offered an idea by saying, "As you consider options, here's one to add to the list."

"I have developed deep appreciation for authenticity – even if it involves a little unrehearsed thinking out loud," Lori says. "I updated a friend recently and she simply said, 'Gosh Lor, I don't think that sounds too good.' Her compassionate honesty invited a more optimistic conversation about treatment options."

And now Grace for Others #4: *Cancer patients can also show kindness.*

"Just as you want to give yourself grace for feeling the emotions you are feeling, you need to have patience and understanding for those around you," says Lisa.

"Remember they struggle. They worry about losing their loved one and facing a future without you. That emotion must be staggering. Make sure to thank others with words and gifts to extend the grace found in appreciation. I buy gifts for friends to thank them for all they have done, and I bring small presents to my chemo nurses and doctors to thank them for their compassion and expertise. Doing all this helps me."

Truth #5: *It's always better to take the helping hand.*

People will want to actively support you, so welcome them. I learned this lesson in a parking lot.

Four Corners of Grace

My battle included strong daily drug treatments at a nearby oncology center. Work colleagues developed a transportation rotation schedule so Becky wouldn't have to drive every day. That felt strange at first, but because their efforts helped my wife who was also a mom of young children, I agreed. Plus, each treatment lasted three hours, so she received much-needed respite from my constant presence.

The first few days, I tolerated the drug therapy well. Soon, though, in the short period between removing the intravenous line from my arm and leaving the clinic, a downward spiral would begin. My goal: tough it out, make it home fast, and sleep. But the time it took for the effects to show up kept growing shorter. I tried but couldn't remain tough long.

My co-worker Robyn's first rotation came in week two. She sat near me and chatted while the drugs dripped into my arm. When the solution bags went empty, the nurse put a Band-Aid on my arm and took my vital signs once more before we headed out the door. All seemed quite routine until we stepped into the bright afternoon sunshine. Robyn had parked in the parking lot's back row, taking one of the few spots available that morning.

She continued to talk while we walked, working hard to keep my spirits up. Rather than take the long route via the sidewalk along the outside of the lot, we walked straight through the parked cars. Usually, a very uneventful venture, unless a person had just received an extremely high dose of cancer-fighting drugs.

Exactly where it happened, I can't recall. But at some point, I felt disoriented and slowed my walking. Robyn, still chatting, kept going. Upon approaching another row of cars, I couldn't see her – or even hear her. All I could see were cars everywhere. I panicked. I was lost. I stopped behind a car's back bumper, and there I stood. Alone. Shaking.

Soon, Robyn came back to find me. "There you are."

As she approached, I swallowed my just-need-to-stay-tough pride and said, "I don't know where I am. Please help me. I can't do this on my own anymore."

She looked me in the eye, and her big smile offered assurance that all would be well. "Oh, c'mon," she said. "It's no big deal. We're almost there."

Then she hooked my arm with hers and steered me toward the car. She continued talking as she drove, still working hard to keep my spirits up. I squeezed her hand the entire way home. The big lesson: It's okay to lean on others during this season.

And now Grace for Others #5: *Find a friend and trust their heart.*

No matter where you are on your journey, you stand just one friend away from eliminating loneliness. Look for someone who will hold your hand and walk with you, talk with you, listen to you, and show up for you. At times, the journey might turn hard, even disorienting. At times, your heart will compel you to share a lot of stuff that's dark and scary. At times, navigating on your own will no longer be an option.

Take, for example, Jim's experience. His buddy Rich submitted regular requests for days off from work after committing to spend significant time with Jim, a lifelong friend battling cancer. Medical treatments, rounds of golf, and strolls down memory lane enabled the two men to enjoy generous helpings of life together. Between moments of laughter, Jim opened his heart to Rich and shared his doubts and fears. The sacredness of those moments created gratitude in Rich's heart. "For me, helping Jim was anything but a burden," he said. "It was an honor to be invited onto the journey."

The right person for this role focuses on the care you need, not the cure. Provides strength, not solutions. Prioritizes well-timed hugs over questions about healing. Loves without expectation, can laugh despite tears, and shows up when you need it – or just because. We will dive even deeper into this role in our Grace for the Journey chapter.

In short, focus more on the helping hand extended to you than on goofy words or reactions people unwittingly share. Because sometimes, when a stormy season just won't go away, you will need someone to stand beside you and hold the umbrella – so the journey can continue.

The people who get it right
include:

Grace for God

-With-

CANCER creates questions. Some have answers; others don't.

What about God? Does the Almighty's role – or presence – in cancer create questions or serve as an answer? Both.

Four Corners of Grace

Serious illness generates strong curiosities. What happens to me if I lose the fight? What if victory stands just an answered prayer away? Rather than projecting yourself into the worst-case or the best-case future scenarios, let's start with the here and now by asking a more direct question: *Where are you in all this, God?*

Welcome to the Grace for God corner, where all are invited to hang out. Have you enjoyed an ongoing relationship with the Father for years already? Come on in. Never given God much thought until now? There's room for you, too. Not sure about any of this but willing to try anything, including reading this chapter? Plenty of space to visit for as long as you'd like.

The reason for the open-door policy: God invites your questions. Your hurts. Your confusion. Your anger. Your fear. Anything you want to say, think, pray, scream, or communicate through tears. While I now also have the perspective of a pastor, this chapter comes from my own experience as a cancer patient.

Let's ask again: *Where are you, God?*

Spiral

Many stories exist about people who pray and receive miracle cures. Folks motivated by good intentions like to share such accounts, believing they provide inspiration. However, I stopped listening after the first few because the silent thought *Why isn't that happening to me?* Grew louder with every miracle report I heard – or was force-fed. Soon, an additional challenge arrived.

My surgery and treatment seemed to work (still true). Prayers answered, right? Well, it's not that tidy. In the first 18 months following my diagnosis, two other people within my relational world – wonderful people – battled the same cancer and eventually lost their fights, despite earnest prayers said by me and others. A full-time ministry role meant that, once folks learned about my cancer, people connected me with their friends and family who had also heard "It's cancer." Ugh. I stopped attending funerals because the thought *Why did this happen to him and not me?* created survivor's guilt that sunk deeper every time news arrived about another loss.

Eventually, and mercifully, the *Why* spiral ended when a close friend shared these words from the Bible:

"For my thoughts are not your thoughts, neither are

your ways my ways,"

declares the LORD.

Isaiah 55:8 (NIV)

Translation: some things will never be known. *Why him and not me?* is an example of a question with no answer – at least none that any human will learn in this life.

For some questions, I feel fine that no answer exists. But it also feels dishonest to deny my desire to know even a little more than I do. Walking through the land of "I don't know" scares me. **And yet,** it's not wrong to want to know more.

So, let's look closer. The same mystery that denies healing to one person can deliver hope to another. Without knowing why or how, people *do* beat cancer – just not predictably or on demand.

Good news: Survival happens with greater average frequency compared to a few decades ago. The problem: No one is "average."

Instead of using an impersonal average, the medical world assigns patient-specific five-year survival rates built from elaborate math models and stated in odds instead of averages. Maybe you know yours. I admit to tuning out of the rest of the conversation after a doctor explained mine. A 50 percent probability of surviving five years sounds too much like a coin flip. The longing to know heads or tails (right now!) created hunger for definitive words, not a percentage. God went on record saying that some things will never be known – whether I would survive five years seemed to fall into this category – so I decided to avoid asking long-term questions that could only produce likelihoods instead of clear answers.

The core reason for averting talk of probabilities: fighting feels so much more productive than gambling. "Probability" or "odds of survival" sounds like casino talk to me. Treatment decisions should not feel like throwing dice. I imagine God rolls His eyes when anyone tries to pin their hopes on coin flips and other wagers.

Goodness

Certainty proves hard to find on a cancer journey. **And yet,** safe assumptions do exist. Start with this one: *God is good.* This will take you closer to understanding where God is on your journey. It's a small step, but a solid starting point.

Another reasonable expectation: If you look for something positive, you often find it. At times, it finds you. Frequently, "it" involves a person.

Coincidentally, God has also gone on record as enjoying making good things happen through people. I noticed that happening, even though my eyes were shut.

As mentioned in the previous chapter, the treatment plan I chose required a harsh, daily drug dose. By the time my then-three-year-old daughter Erin arrived home from preschool every day, my cycle of nausea, chills, and shakes had ended with high fever. Like an overheated car that ran out of gas, I lay motionless in bed and repeatedly pleaded with God to help me fall asleep, even though voicing that desire proved strenuous. *If I can fall asleep in the next thirty minutes, I think I can make it. Please help.*

"Where's Daddy?" Erin asked.

"In bed," Becky said.

"What's he doing?"

"Trying to take a nap. Let's be quiet because he needs to sleep, but he can't."

Erin sensed that Daddy needed someone to do something to help him. Every afternoon that entire month of treatment, she would quietly open the door and, with the graceful motions of a tiny ballerina, scamper across the floor, and make the short hop up onto the bed, landing as gently as a silk scarf. She then snuggled ever so lightly against me and likely wondered why I felt so hot. It worked every time; I fell asleep. I had never expected that God would deliver profound goodness through a young girl still learning her ABCs.

And yet, give God the grace to believe that He's working in ways you might not immediately notice, even if you have only enough energy to squeeze out tiny belief. He can work in small increments.

What would happen if you decided to attribute God's presence to the good things that happen outside your control? It won't take away the cancer, but it can take away the loneliness. A preschooler taught me that God remains close enough to hear me when I can barely whisper. In some mysterious way, such awareness allowed me to feel like I had received help carrying the weight of the cancer burden. When I started looking for the good, it more frequently appeared. Was an answer to *Where are you in all this?* beginning to emerge for me? Might one be beginning to develop for you?

More questions likely exist, too. Ask them. God wants you to so that the two of you can talk – in whatever way works for you. God's a good listener.

"Every day I receive a text with Bible verses from a friend," says Lisa. "I cherish them because they help me put everything back into perspective and bring me back to God."

An example verse might help.

Remember the directive from my doctor? He said, "Eliminate stress from your life." Well, there's a statement in the Bible that says we can cast all our anxieties upon God because he (God) cares about us (1 Peter 5:7). Admittedly, how to make that happen can feel a bit fuzzy. But God seems to want to help fill the prescription needed, and that's a good thing.

Trust

Give God the grace to believe He's working in more ways than you can see, hear, or know. Such trust, such belief, can serve as the first step toward grace for God – suspecting that He's doing stuff behind the scenes. Again, it's a small step, but a good one to try. This email message from a friend named Cheryl served as an example of a peek at a different scene that I re-read often when wondering where God was and what He was doing:

Without you even knowing it through your ordeal, you have helped to create relationships with God that were not there before. Let me explain.

A couple of nights ago, Chris [Cheryl's husband] *and I went out for dinner, and I told him that you received good news about your lymph nodes. He said he was so happy and that he had been praying for you! It brought a tear to my eye; he said this made him want to pray more about other stuff, too.*

You likely never knew that your sickness would move people closer to God. I hope this story helps in your journey with God; I know it has mine.

"I can say that I never gave up on God or got mad at him or blamed him for my cancer," says Lisa. "A friend whose spouse was diagnosed with cancer shortly before me said he turned away from

God when he got sick. I never could do that. I need God too much."

Answer

To help us pull this chapter together, let's look at a Bible story that definitively answers the question: *Where are you, God?*

An entire population of people – the Israelites – served as slaves for another country and prayed for that reality to end. Eventually, God helped them leave the oppression and go to another land, which involved a challenging and confusing journey through the desert. They weren't sure what path they were on and had no idea how long their grueling walk would last. The big picture of this story is easy for us to read about but must have been frustratingly impossible to comprehend while it took place. Sound familiar?

The Almighty did more than just open the border for them. During the days, He went ahead of them in the form of a cloud that led them in the direction they needed to travel. Every night, He transformed into a pillar of fire behind them; the dark can be quite scary. Plus, as most security lights prove, the illumination served as a deterrent to potential attackers. This day-night presence rhythm served as assurance to the Israelites that they were not alone, which gave them the hope they needed to complete their journey.

Your days likely seem cloudy and overcast, probably stormy. Nights may feature burning anxiety. The Bible story suggests that it's exactly in such times that God shows up.

A cancer diagnosis quickly expands to become a big picture that's larger than any of us can comprehend. Doctors know more about cancer than you do. Fortunately, God knows even more.

This chapter started with the question *Where?* The answer is *With.*

God is *with* you every step, every day, and every night. He walks *with* you – but will not force Himself upon you. Instead, He invites you into this corner. Stay here long enough, share your hard questions, speak the truth about how you feel, then give Him the grace to show Himself. You will discover He provides the hope you need to continue your journey.

So do not fear, for I am with you; do not be
dismayed, for I am your God.
I will strengthen you and help you; I will uphold
you with my righteous right hand.
Isaiah 41:10 (NIV)

Questions I want to ask God:

Grace for the Journey

-Prepare-

LET'S catch our breath and develop a travel plan.

With any adventure, you can prepare for nearly anything – but only if you know what's coming. Realistically, no one readies themselves for a cancer journey before the unwanted news arrives. Why would you?

Four Corners of Grace

You heard "It's cancer," so the time has arrived to prepare. Several areas deserve consideration; you will feel better about the road ahead when you respond to prompts in the sections that follow. Making choices now is a grace-filled way to launch this journey you did not choose, yet now must travel. Your fight is with the cancer, not the road that carries you through it.

It's time to get busy.

Trust

To fight cancer means you will face many new decisions. While I wanted to believe my common sense and discernment skills would carry me through just fine, the emotional curveball thrown at me by a cancer diagnosis made even simple choices seem hard. For that reason, seriously consider whose voice you will trust. This doesn't mean that you should ignore everyone else's input. It does mean, though, that you recognize the need for people you can count on to speak into – or make – decisions when you 1) can't, 2) won't, or 3) don't know how.

This inner circle needs only a few chairs; maybe just one or two. Too many voices create unwelcome chaos – and the possibility of differing opinions will mean you'll have to make the decision after all. Ugh.

An example will help. Following surgery, my lead physician referred me to another specialist who suggested an aggressive, experimental treatment. The specialist then encouraged me to seek a second opinion – a fairly common practice. The next doctor advised against the experimental treatment. One for the treatment. One against. What?

Confused, I returned to my lead doctor who said solid cases existed for both opinions. Two reactions happened next. First, I expressed how much I appreciated the subjectivity involved with cancer. Second, I refused to let my lead physician remain undecided, as clarified by a somewhat colorful reminder of the trust I had already placed in him. (Rest of the story: he smiled and said that I should pursue the aggressive treatment because it matched my intensity and, most important, I'd never forgive myself if I did anything less. He was right.)

Determine who you trust and stick with your choice. Consistency will lead to greater confidence when future decisions must be made, especially those that show up unexpectedly.

Midway through my treatment course, adverse effects arrived. The ability to have a conversation disappeared, as did any modicum of decision-making for myself. In a meeting held by the center's medical staff to determine whether to continue my treatments, the nursing staff and pharmaceutical company researcher (monitoring the experimental drug regimen) opined to stop. My physician asked Becky to make the final decision, an offer she rejected. "Oh no," she said. "You're the doctor, and we've trusted you this far. You make the decision."

Numerous non-medical decisions will seem to pop up like weeds in an empty field. How do I tell people? Who do I tell? How does my insurance work? What about non-medical options? How long should I wait before asking? Do I have to go to that gathering? What clothes should I wear? Is it okay for me to feel like this? When do I contact the nurse? How will I get to treatment? Who will take care of my responsibilities? These questions represent a small sample; prepare for this list to frequently replenish itself. Thus, the need to lean on others.

After you select who you will trust, let them know that you'd like to count on them. The right people embrace such an honor. Lisa points us toward three groups where candidates exist. "I don't know how people get through something like this without their faith (church), family and friends, and a doctor you trust," she said.

Make a list but keep it short to start. The people I trust *most* to help me on this journey:

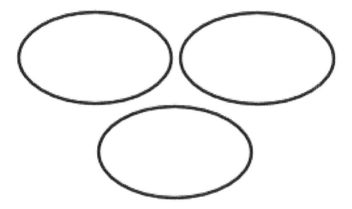

Meet with each person you named to discuss the confidence you feel in him or her. Consider saying, "You will help me beat this!" Prepare to enjoy a heart-bonding conversation to follow.

Internal battles

As if cancer isn't enough, other challenges will also burrow into your psyche. Many of these unwelcome intruders lead with "I don't..." statements. Turn them away with "I will..." resolutions. Let's look at four.

1) Loneliness

As discussed earlier, loneliness makes its presence felt through fear, as in *I don't have anyone who understands me and can walk through this with me.*

Such trepidation quickly evaporates when you reach out your hand to other people, regardless of how much that hand might shake. The resolutions that follow will serve you well and will help dismiss loneliness:

I will place trust in a few others.

I will be deeply honest with at least one or two people, meaning I will describe my fears, my feelings, and my future.

I will not self-label as a burden to others, which would lead me to believe others don't care about me.

I will accept help, especially the gift of presence – I will not hide (with the option to avoid certain people, when needed).

I will find one or two people I can call at any time when I feel down – and I will call them.

2) Waiting

Cancer involves significant waiting periods – for test results, for appointments, for treatments, for updates, the list goes on. These empty times, when the silence begins to feel deafening, invite speculation that tends to turn negative, such as *I don't know what's going on, so it must be bad.*

Unchecked and on its own, waiting morphs into worry. So, occupy the waiting by scrolling through this list and selecting those options that engage you:

I will remind myself that nothing happens fast in diagnosing, confirming, treating, or recovering.

I will invite someone else to wait with me (see previous section).

I will continue to trust caregivers', friends', and my decisions.

I will think about responses to all possible scenarios, including both positive and negative outcomes.

I will involve myself in _____ (fill in the blank) *as I wait, to avoid empty idle time.*

3) Survival

Let's dive deeper. Some cancer diagnoses are much grimmer than others. Mine started rough but changed, Lori's has gone up and down multiple times, and Lisa consistently faces steep challenges. Any discussion about worry must address THE big concern that few people articulate: *I don't know if I have a reasonable chance to beat this.*

After hearing about so many cases when a hopeless diagnosis proved wrong, knowing people who beat intimidating odds, and a few unexplainable miracles, the answer is always *Yes, you do have a reasonable chance.* To galvanize that conviction, even if pure defiance must emerge to muster up the courage, embrace these resolutions:

I will consider all possibilities, not just the dark ones.

I will make plans for a future that involves my full recovery.

I will talk with others about what I plan for the day I win this battle.

4) Relapse

"Once you have had cancer, you always have it in the back of your mind that it will come back," says Lisa. "You worry that the other shoe will drop." The lingering suspicion often sounds like this: *I don't know if I will ever feel healthy again.*

Plan to push such fear into the far back of your mind when you adopt strong statements about life with deliberate, declarative purpose:

I will refuse to let cancer take me out early, so I will pursue joy (see next section) – *knowing it will energize my journey through cancer and my life after cancer.*

I will take every chance I receive to do what I want to do, whether it's during the active battle, after treatments end, or when the day comes that I hear the words "remission" or "no trace of disease."

I will live for today, every day – and love other people well.

Everywhere and every day

Sometimes after a new purchase, you start to notice how many others bought the same thing. In like fashion, you will spot cancer more than ever. Sure, COVID stole the stage for an act or two, but cancer still receives top billing for the most frequent serious health issue – or so it appears. "It seems like every time I open a book or turn on a movie or

Netflix show, someone is dying of cancer," says Lisa. "I find that frustrating."

Or triggering. Maybe maddening. Even anxiety-producing.

Lisa describes how noticing cancer when it appears can turn into searching for it: "Every time someone tells me they know of someone who has passed away, I find myself asking them, 'Was it cancer?' It usually is, and my stomach drops. I wish I could stop asking that question, but I can't."

Cancer seems to exist everywhere because it does, in fact, afflict so many. No words can change that reality.

And yet, a different option exists. "Try to find joy and happiness in every day," Lisa says. "Do what makes you feel good without feeling guilty about it."

What gives you joy? Lisa and Lori suggest replacing one word so the question becomes *Who gives you joy?* Let's be honest, some people give life, while others take it out of those around them. Your cancer will quickly clarify in which of those two groups every person you know belongs.

Four Corners of Grace

Imagine the impact of telling someone "Time with you is very life-giving to me."

List out the people who you need to hear that message from you:

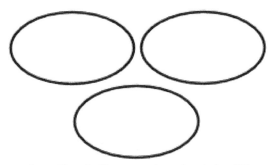

(Suggestion: Don't list people who take life out of you, in case someone flips through the pages of this book.)

Let's go back to *what* gives you joy. For some, soul-warming delight comes from sunsets, piano music, and writing. Lisa receives energy from time with people and from giving them gifts. Name the experiences that make you smile, even as you write them below:

_____ _____ _____

When items show up on such a list, they become more likely to happen. For that reason, consider these three (or more) as priority to-do items.

A special club

Until now, one group has received only brief mention – other cancer patients. You will meet many in the battle and some who have already won their fights. There's inspiration and understanding and acceptance to be gained, so ready yourself.

Four Corners of Grace

You'll feel it in the gentle touch of a fellow patient, when you hear words that create an instant bond, or see glimpses of resilience in their eyes. Let down your guard and allow others to feel, hear, and see those things in you, too. When you engage someone else with the tenderness that only a fellow patient can provide, you will experience brief but deep fulfillment. These moments have purpose. For you. For the other person. Talk, ask, listen. For a brief period, maybe longer, enjoy precious time with someone who understands.

As I was drafting this chapter, I spoke at a church meeting held for caregivers and patients. While describing a challenging moment I faced fighting cancer, I felt the all-too-familiar shakes that had occurred during treatment many years ago. Folks who attended the meeting were quick and gracious to share understanding for how emotions stay with a person, emerging at unanticipated times and in unexpected ways. In a room of strangers, I felt loved by friends. You'll find this often as you interact with others who travel a similar yet different path. This club, in which you now hold lifelong membership, serves as a safe place.

.....

Earlier, you learned about the rough side effects of the treatment course I chose and the meeting that took place with the medical center staff. Later that day, Becky tried to explain how serious the situation had turned, but I couldn't comprehend what she shared. One comment did, though, finesse its way into my awareness: "If they see you shuffling when you walk, they will immediately stop everything."

As I entered the treatment facility the next day, filled with resolve to complete the journey, I lifted my knees in exaggerated form with every stride. Yes, I high stepped into the office. Still struggling to talk or understand a conversation, I remained willing to give it my all so I could finish.

A few days later, the adverse effects subsided. After receiving the last treatment, I walked with a normal gait and big smile into the nurses' break room and thanked them for not giving up on me.

Keep walking, my friend. No matter what it takes. Keep walking.

To strengthen my resolve, I will:

Four Corners of Grace

For Caregivers

-Together-

FROM Becky, David's wife:

Caregiver, you matter more than you'll ever realize. As one who has played the role you find yourself in, I understand and appreciate your importance in the battle against cancer. Your work won't be easy, but it can still be good – and extremely life-giving to the person you assist.

This book opened with David walking through the front door to say, "It's cancer." Neither of us knew anything about the journey we faced. Not even the first steps. Or the sidesteps that would be needed. Or the steps backward we wouldn't see until too late. Honestly, we tripped over our feet more than once because cancer's rhythm can change everything without warning.

For example, at one point David's tastebuds decided to malfunction. Water suddenly had the flavor of a car tire. An orange sports drink worked, but only for a single day. I returned the remaining bottles and exchanged them for cherry. The next day I swapped them for lemon. And then the next flavor, on and on. This didn't seem like a big deal until the store manager asked me why I was making the daily replacements. Even though it's my husband's cancer, it was hard for me to talk about it. But I had to. Following our chat, the manager told me to skip the checkout lanes in future visits and even offered to stock different flavors. Plenty of good people still exist to support you in your important role.

David's needs shifted based on procedures, treatments, good news, rough news, and new challenges. His emotions wobbled. Mine careened as I constantly pushed myself to do something – okay, anything – that could help. He fought the disease; I fought for him. Imperfectly many times, which is perfectly fine.

Four Corners of Grace

Please hold tight to that grace-filled truth: *Imperfect is perfectly fine.*

Thank you for reading this chapter. You likely serve as either a caregiver or a cancer patient – or know someone in one of those roles. Whatever brought you here, I want to encourage caregivers. Assuming that's you, please let yourself receive my encouragement. Whether you're a spouse, family member, or close friend, this chapter will speak to you.

To start: Wow! The amount of trust placed in you defies measurement. You must be a tremendous person with a huge heart. To help another person navigate a cancer journey shows that you are special.

Get used to hearing these words because they are true: Your strength, your care, and your compassion provide powerful therapy. Not that this will ever be easy.

One evening during David's treatment season, we sat in bed talking. Well, I sat as he leaned on my shoulder and dozed off. While placing his head – flush with fever – onto a pillow I whispered, "I want the old you back."

You likely feel the same about the person for whom you provide care. Something inside you, though, tells you that won't happen. Prepare for this to be true. Does anyone bounce back from a cancer battle as the same person they were before? Not likely, and that's okay because that's how life works. Some changes occur for the better. Both

Four Corners of Grace

David and I developed stronger resilience, deeper appreciation, and broader perspective.

Should you continue to hope for a complete victory? Of course! Work hard for it? You bet. Along the way, embrace right here, right now.

Here's why. Focus too much on how it will end, and you'll appear to walk too far ahead. David needed me with him step by step. Let's you and I take four steps together right now to help your journey make a little more sense. Or maybe a lot of sense.

Step 1 – Count on confusion.

Medical terms. Specialists. Insurance. Treatments. Nutrition. At-home care. Visits. Transportation. Finances. Family. Friends. The internet. Cancer triggers plenty of confusion. All of this happens to everyone; when you feel confused it shows you're paying attention to reality.

So, what can you do? Call people you know who have 1) expertise they can share, 2) experience learning all this stuff, or 3) work in an area you need to understand. On these calls, ask all your questions and then ask for different explanations if you don't understand what a person tells you. As the store manager showed me, people lean toward helping someone who's a caregiver. You just need to ask.

Remember: Your strength, your care, and your compassion provide powerful therapy.

Step 2 – Go easy on yourself because it is a difficult road you travel.

Four Corners of Grace

Worry felt like an unwelcome, live-in guest. Sure, moments arrived when thoughts turned toward the worst case – life without David. He and I talked about it, which helped to not let such a dark picture linger in my mind too long. But worry is a category that includes much more. Let's look at answers to a few big questions I asked – and that you might wonder about, too. The answers will give you confidence.

What if I'm not doing something well, seeing something right, or making a good decision?

Remember that the fight is against cancer, a disease so complex that no reliable cure exists. Mistakes, misunderstandings, and mishaps of all sorts will happen. That's true about life in any context. As long as you don't give up, you will bring needed strength to the fight. Imperfection is perfectly fine, I've heard.

What about the times when he or she goes quiet, possibly not wanting to talk to me?

The person you're caring for feels vulnerable, and that's a hard thing to feel in addition to possibly feeling physically lousy, out of control, and at the whim of a disease that robs life and destroys healthy cells. The chapter on Grace for Me gives them permission to feel and cope in whatever way works. Similar permission from you – spoken with grace – will eliminate tension and allow you both to relax.

But am I doing a good job?

It's been said that 80 percent of success is showing up. For that reason, yes. However, in the role of a caregiver, you will likely not receive appreciation often enough. No one starts this journey fully prepared to deal with everything that's ahead. But you *are* ready to do and say and learn and help to the best of your ability.

After all, your strength, your care, and your compassion provide powerful therapy.

Step 3 – Take breaks to avoid breaking down. Do everything on your own and eventually you will grow weary – or worse. While the person you care for has placed tremendous trust in you, determine now that you will not attempt a solo act.

When others want to help, let them – with your guidance, of course. When someone asks what he or she can do, speak up – with specifics. What does all this mean? Lisa provides ideas for what other people can do to show their support for the cancer patient – support that will also help you:

1. Text, call, or send cards periodically.

2. Prepare meals, baked goods, or a gift to a subscription-based meal service since it may be hard for the patient or caregiver to cook.

3. Provide gift cards for restaurants to give the entire family a reason to look forward to meals.

4. Arrange for a subscription to a video streaming service.

5. Clean the house or arrange for a cleaning service.

6. Take the patient to a movie, a garden, or anywhere fun.

7. Drive the patient to treatment; set up a transportation schedule involving several friends.

8. Show up with a plant or flowers.

9. Purchase an airline ticket so a family member can visit.

10. Run errands with the patient or the caregiver – it gives everyone a break.

Please take care of yourself. You are too important to lose. When you need a day away, take it. Need someone to just listen? Call a friend and tell them you want to do the talking. Make sure to get sleep, activity, and good food. Or food that's not good for you, if that's what you need. Time for a confession: A friend provided a meal for our family that included a large chocolate cake, which I consumed on my own. A girl's gotta do what a girl's gotta do, right?

You have full permission to speak up, put your feet up, eat up, or do anything else to keep you going. Why? You are essential because your strength, your care, and your compassion provide powerful therapy.

Step 4 – "Together" will happen because of you.
The resilience needed to stand and fight cancer sometimes requires tapping into someone else's strength – that's the sacred role you play. The Bible says that it's not good for a person to be alone. Multiply that truth by 100 for someone on a cancer journey.

Four Corners of Grace

The road ahead has double-wide lanes; it's meant to be traveled with someone. You can stand when he can't. You can make decisions when the person you're caring for cannot. You can smile when they just aren't able.

When you grip a patient's trembling hand with your own, goodness flows like water from where there's much to where there's less. No greater calling, no higher honor exists than the opportunity to selflessly share life. The difficult path you will blaze to answer this calling is, indeed, a high road.

Early one afternoon, at a time when he typically slept, David wandered into our backyard partially dressed, fully awake, yet completely unaware of his surroundings. He loves caring for the lawn, so maybe that's what beckoned him outdoors. *The old*

116

you is still in there somewhere, I thought when I found him after a few tense moments of searching. Without saying a word, I slipped my right hand into his left, and we walked for a little while longer, eventually making our way back into the house where he could get the rest he needed, I could give him all the care I knew how to, and the two of us could continue to fight cancer.

The ways of grace this book shares guided us through the battle. Help from others proved invaluable. God's love proved indescribable. That's big picture perspective. The road you're on, though, involves just one step at a time. That's the challenge.

So, every time you feel confused, face difficulty, or experience fatigue – and you will likely encounter many such moments – remember that you always have one more move. Grab your person's hand, gently of course, but in a way that says: *I'm not letting go, and I'm not letting you go through this alone. We have a journey to travel. Together.*

Your strength, your care, and your compassion provide powerful therapy. For the person you give care to – and for you.

Other books by David Staal

Four Corner of Grace: When You Lose Your Job

Four Corners of Grace: When Suicide Takes Someone You Love

Show Up: Step Out of Your Story and Into Someone Else's

Show Up: Student Edition

Made in the USA
Monee, IL
12 July 2023

39044950R00075